MODERN
FILM
SCRIPTS

IKIRU

a film by

Akira Kurosawa

Edited and with an introduction
by Donald Richie

Simon and Schuster, New York

Published by Simon and Schuster
Rockefeller Center, 630 Fifth Avenue
New York, N.Y. 10020
First printing

The photographs in this edition are reproduced through the courtesy of the Toho Company Ltd, Kurosawa Productions, and UniJapan Film, Tokyo

Frontispiece: Akira Kurosawa directing *Ikiru*

Library of Congress Catalog Card Number: 68-27594

Manufactured in Great Britain by Villiers Publications Ltd,
London NW5

CONTENTS

INTRODUCTION

Akira Kurosawa's *Ikiru* is a cinematic expression of modern existential thought. It consists of a restrained affirmation within the context of a giant negation. What it says in starkly lucid terms is that 'life' is meaningless. At the same time, one man's life can acquire meaning when he undertakes to perform some task which *to him* is meaningful. What anyone else thinks about that man's life is beside the point, even ludicrous. The meaning of his life is what he commits the meaning of his life to be. There is nothing else.

Richard Brown

'Sometimes I think of my death,' Kurosawa has written: 'I think of ceasing to be . . . and it is from these thoughts that *Ikiru* came.' The story of a man who knows that he is going to die, the film is a search for affirmation. It is found in the moral message of the film, which, in turn, is contained in the title — '*ikiru*' is the intransitive verb meaning '*to live.*' This itself is the affirmation: existence is enough. But to live, one must live entirely and, at the same time, must give this life whatever meaning it is to have. This is the lesson learned by Kanji Watanabe, the petty official whose life and death give meaning to this film.

In the opening sections of the film a doctor asks an intern: 'What would you do if you had only half a year to live?' Kurosawa answers the question by showing what Watanabe does and by insisting that we both observe and share each of the snares and delusions to which man in crisis is subject.

Watanabe's first reaction is fear. In bed that night he pulls the covers over his head and cries, and the camera — moving from effect to cause — turns to the wall where his letter of commendation for twenty-five years of civil service is hanging.

He next attempts to lose himself in the only family he has, his son and daughter-in-law, but he cannot. Over the years they have become alienated. Finding no solace there, he begins, for the first time in his life, to doubt. To doubt means to feel, to begin to live.

He doubts the office, doubts his twenty-five years of service, doubts his family. Awakened by the knowledge of his death, he realizes for the first time that he is freed of all habits and, hence, of all comforts. A mindless acceptance of bureaucratic routine, an easy and meaningless relationship with his son, these are no longer enough. Freedom is his, has always been, he can now no longer avoid it.

He decides to live by spending his last months in pleasure. Drawing his savings from the bank, he goes for a wild time on the town. But pleasure too is no solace. Dead drunk to the world outside, cold sober within, he ends in the small morning hours singing a song from his youth — wondering, helpless, loving life, conscious of every passing moment.

He does not again fall prey to empty pleasure. Rather, he decides to devote himself to someone, and chooses a girl from his office. For a short time he is happy, enjoying with her a kind of second childhood. Yet this too is delusion. He has forgotten that she too is human and cannot hence exist simply as an object for his own passion to live. Yet it is she who — on their last meeting — gives him the clue he needs: he must act, and this he at last realizes.

Watanabe discovers himself through 'doing'. Like Dostoevsky's Myushikin, like Sartre's Roquetin, or Camus's Rambert, he has discovered what it means to be and the pain is so exquisite that it drives him to action, to conceive a plan which will 'save' him. Perhaps without even grasping the truth he is acting out, he behaves as though he believes that it is action alone which matters; that a man is not his thoughts, nor his intentions, but *is* simply what he *does*. In the most simple of terms (and this is how he seems to think of it) this action is a form of insurance against his ' having lived in vain.'

He rescues from certain oblivion a petition, one which has long waited on his desk and the desks of others, for turning a section of waste land into a park. He flings himself upon it and with desperate energy and persistence he fights all obstacles to its realization. Against official indifference, active discouragement, even intimidation, he forces the park into being. And only then, we are given to understand, does he die.

Kurosawa shows us all of this indirectly. The first half of the film is concerned with a definition of Watanabe's past and present. The opening shot, for example, is an X-ray plate. We are shown Watanabe's organic inside before we are shown his outside; we are shown cancer as literally defining the man. In the same way, throughout the first half of the film, we are shown his body and what it does; in the second half the body has disappeared and we are shown — through the observations and conversations of others — his soul, what remains of him. Or, to put it another way, we have seen what is real — Watanabe and his reactions to approaching death. Now, in the second half, we see illusion — the reactions of others, their excuses, their accidental stumblings on the truth, their final rejection of both the truth and of Watanabe as he truly is.

Perhaps these are the reasons that Kurosawa so insists upon the ' reality ' of the first half of the film and uses so brilliantly all his technical resources to convince us of this reality. Not that he insists upon the literal. Far from it — he, along with the writer whom Watanabe meets, knows that ' art is not direct.' Rather, he orders Watanabe's life through selection of detail, at the same time observing this life through a variety of cinematic resources, all of them intended to make us feel what Watanabe is feeling.

For example, in the opening scenes of the film, the man who will eventually replace Watanabe looks towards his desk, but Watanabe is not there. He is at the hospital. The punctuation of these short scenes shows Kurosawa's intentions.

Man looks at desk — cut — empty desk — cut — Watanabe in hospital corridor — dissolve — Watanabe in waiting-room, then standing up to get a drink of water.

One would have expected the dissolve to occur between the desk and corridor scenes. It is, after all, a new location and, presumably, some time has elapsed. Kurosawa, however, thinks of it in another way. He is saying that the underling, desk, and Watanabe are all of a unit, that they all belong to the office. However, (dissolve), something odd and important will happen to Watanabe in the hospital. In a way, Watanabe is already a different man in the hospital.

Again, the final scene in this hospital sequence has been, once more, an X-ray close-up, and the only sound has been that of the buzzing of the fluorescent light. There is then a direct cut to Watanabe walking along a busy street. As we watch, we feel that something is wrong with the scene, though we do not know what it is until, with a great roar, a truck nearly runs down the dazed Watanabe. Then we see that until the noise of the truck, the scene had been completely silent, despite the cars and people in it. It is as though we, like Watanabe, had become numb through shock. In such ways are we led to empathize, to feel for him, and hence to feel for ourselves.

In speaking of his own death, Kurosawa has said: 'There is, I feel, so much for me to do. I keep feeling I have lived so little. Then I become thoughtful, but not sad.' This thoughtfulness is seen at its strongest in the second half of the film. Watanabe is dead, only what he has done remains behind. In flash-back we see what happened to him. As he grows more and more ill, his face becomes more and more determined. He carries the look of the girl in Kurosawa's early film, *No Regrets For Our Youth,* when she says: 'I want to find out what it is to live.' During the wake which comprises the second half of the picture, and its successive revelations, it gradually becomes clear where this thoughtfulness is leading. Watanabe really found his vindication through pure action alone. The park was only a pretext for this action. It makes no difference whether the department of parks or the Deputy Mayor claim credit; even the small voice of the one fellow-worker who stands up for the dead Watanabe has no real meaning.

The only meaning is that Watanabe made a meaning for his life. In his own way he discovered a way to be responsible both for and to others; he found a way to vindicate his death and, more important, his life. He found out what it means to live.

It is quite possible that Kurosawa would disagree with this interpretation of his film. Certainly, he does not think of himself as being an existentialist. At the same time, however, throughout his films, as throughout the works of many artists of Japan, there runs a moral assumption which has much in common with the existential thesis. *Rashomon* questions all truth and affirms only that choice is always present; *Stray Dog* reveals cop and robber as responsible for each other; in *I Live in Fear* (related to *Ikiru,* in a way its negative image) the hero, having felt the lash of freedom, experienced the terrible responsibilities of his own actions, ends in a madhouse; in *Seven Samurai* only action matters — whether one was a good samurai or a bad robber is meaningless. As in the novels of Dostoevsky — Kurosawa's favourite author — we see layer after layer peeled away until man stands alone, completely responsible for himself, and responsible for the choice which forever renews itself.

This, Kurosawa shares in common with other directors of his generation — with Bresson, Antonioni, Bergman, Bunuel.

And in *Ikiru* he moves further, delves deeper, and finds an affirmation, a truth beyond despair.

DONALD RICHIE

CREDITS:

Directed by	Akira Kurosawa
Scenario by	Akira Kurosawa, Shinobu Hashimoto and Hideo Oguni
Photography by	Asakazu Nakai
Music by	Fumio Hayasaka
Art Direction by	So Matsuyama
Lighting by	Shigeru Mori
Sound Recording by	Fumio Yanoguchi
Produced by	Shojiro Motoki
Production	Toho Company Ltd
Length	3,918 metres
Running time	143 mins
First released	October 9th, 1952
Distributed in England by	Connoisseur Films Ltd.
Distributed in America by	Brandon Films, Inc.

CAST:

Kanji Watanabe, Chief, Citizens' Section	Takashi Shimura
Mitsuo, his son	Nobuo Kaneko
Kazue, Mitsuo's wife	Kyoko Seki
Kiichi, Kanji's elder brother	Makoto Kobori
Tatsu, Kiichi's wife	Kumeko Urabe
The maid	Yoshie Minami
Toyo Odagiri	Miki Odagiri
Ono, sub-section chief	Kamatari Fujiwara
Saito, subordinate clerk	Minosuke Yamada
Sakai, assistant	Haruo Tanaka
Ohara, assistant	Bokuzen Hidari
Kimura, assistant	Shinichi Himori
Deputy Mayor	Nobuo Nakamura
City Councillor	Kazuo Abe
Doctor	Masao Shimizu
Young Doctor	Isao Kimura
Patient	Atsushi Watanabe
Writer	Yunosuke Ito
Hostess	Yatsuko Tanami
Newspaperman	Fuyuki Murakami
Gang-boss	Seiji Miyaguchi
Gang-member	Daisuke Kato
Policeman	Ichiro Chiba
Housewives	Kin Sugai, Eiko Miyoshi, Fumiko Homma

IKIRU

Titles white on black; slow, rather melancholy music; then, a close-up of an X-ray negative while a voice is heard explaining.

NARRATOR *off*: This is an X-ray picture of a stomach; it belongs to the man this story is about. Symptoms of cancer are there but he doesn't yet know anything about it.

Cut to the City Hall, the desk of KANJI WATANABE, *Chief of the Citizen's Section. He sits behind a desk piled high with papers and is busy putting his seal to various documents. Then he stops and looks at his watch. Cut to the front of the office, the information desk; a number of women are talking with* SAKEI, *the Section Clerk. On the desk is the notice: 'THIS WINDOW IS FOR YOU. IT IS YOUR LINK WITH THE CITY HALL. WE WELCOME BOTH REQUESTS AND COMPLAINTS.'*

WOMEN: And my child got a rash from that water . . . It smells bad too . . . There are millions of mosquitoes . . . Why can't you do something with the land? It would make a good playground.

SAKEI *excuses himself and goes to* WATANABE'S *desk, telling him that some petitioners from Kuroe-cho are there.* WATANABE *tells him to send them to the Public Works Section, then looks at his watch again.*

NARRATOR *off*: This is the main character of our story, but he's not very interesting yet. He's just passing the time, wasting it, rather. It would be difficult to say that he is really alive.

WATANABE *suddenly looks up at the sound of laughter. Cut to the office where everyone is looking at the office-girl* TOYO, *who has suddenly broken into laughter.* ONO, *the Assistant Chief, speaks sharply to her, telling her to please watch her behaviour during working hours.*

Cut back to WATANABE, *who takes off his glasses.*

TOYO : But it was funny.

ONO : What was?

TOYO : This joke that someone passed round.

ONO : Read it then.

Cut to TOYO *standing up. She hesitates, then begins to read from a newspaper clipping.*

TOYO *reading* : You've never had a day off, have you? No. Why? Are you indispensable? No, I just don't want them to find out they can do without me.

She laughs, but no one else does. Cut to WATANABE, *who has been listening. Now he puts his glasses on again and goes back to stamping papers.*

NARRATOR *off* : This is pretty bad. He is like a corpse and actually he has been dead for the past twenty-five years. Before that he had some life in him. He even tried to work.

WATANABE *wants to clean his seal and is looking for some paper. He opens a desk drawer full of old documents. The top one reads A PLAN TO INCREASE OFFICE EFFICIENCY. He tears off the first page, cleans his seal, throws the paper into the basket, and goes on stamping, while the* NARRATOR *continues off.*

NARRATOR *off* : But now he neither tries nor even wants to. His ambitions have been well smothered by City Hall. But, he's busy — oh, very busy. Still, he is doing little. He has to keep busy simply to stay where he is. Is this as it should be?

WATANABE *seems to feel uncomfortable; he takes his tablets, and drinks some water.*

NARRATOR *off* : But before he begins to think seriously, his stomach must get worse and more useless hours must accumulate.

Cut to the WOMEN *from Kuroe-cho arriving at the office of the Public Works Section where the* CLERK *in charge*

says that he is sorry, but this matter comes under the authority of the Parks Section. Wipe to the Parks Section where the CLERK *is telling them that the matter seems to be concerned with saniiation, hence they had better go to the Health Centre. Dissolve into the Centre where they are told that the Sanitation Section will take care of them; a lively fugue is built under these scenes, based on a motif from the opening music. Wipe to the Sanitation Section where they are told to go to the Environmental Health Section. Wipe to that Section where they are told they must go to the Anti-Epidemics Office. Wipe to that Office where a* CLERK, *hearing it is about mosquitoes, directs them to the Pest Control Section. Wipe to that section where a* CLERK *swats a fly before directing them to the Sewage Section. Wipe to the Sewage Section where a* CLERK *says that theirs was indeed formerly a sewage area but that a road ran over it, so, unless the Road Section approves . . . Wipe to the Road Section where they are told that since the City Planning Department's policy is not yet established, they had best go there first. Wipe to the Planning Department where they learn that the Fire Department had wanted the section reclaimed because of such poor water facilities, so they had better go there. Wipe to the Fire Department where the* CLERK *says that it is nonsense, they do not want dirty water, it would ruin their hoses. Now if they had a swimming pool or something there, then the Fire Department might be interested. Wipe to the Children's Welfare Officer at the Educational Section, who tells them that such a big problem as this should be taken up with the City Councillor. Wipe to the Councillor's office. He is saying that he will give his personal introduction to the Deputy Mayor. Wipe to the office of that official, who is saying that he is truly happy when citizens take it upon themselves to make such suggestions, and for that reason they have established a special Citizens' Section. Wipe back to the Citizens' Section.* SAKEI *is again at the desk and does not remember them; he tells them to go to the Public Works Section. The* WOMEN *become angry.*

WOMEN: What do you think we are anyway? What does this sign here mean? Isn't it your section's responsibility? Don't worry, we won't bother you again . . .

They start to leave. After a moment's hesitation, he runs after them, and catches them at the door.

SAKEI: Just a moment, please. I'm sorry. You see, our Section Chief is out today. If you could possibly just submit a written petition.

All the staff stand up, to watch the women go.

Quick shot of WATANABE'S *empty desk.*

Dissolve to the office. Two of the staff are eating their lunch and drinking tea as they talk, back to camera.

SAITO: It is certainly unusual for him to be out.

ONO: Well, he hasn't been looking too well lately.

SAITO: Yes, but it wouldn't be good if he stays out too long.

ONO: Funny, though. Certainly he wouldn't take sick-leave just for a cold. Besides, I need his seal.

Cut to another part of the office. Two other members of the staff are eating their lunch, while they talk.

KIMURA: It's too bad though. Another month and he'd have had thirty years without one day off.

OHARA: Yes, but you notice that now he's away certain people seem a lot happier. Well, everyone wants to get on in the world.

Cut to another part of the office, where they are also having lunch.

SAKEI: Wonder what that medicine is he's always taking.

TOYO: Something for his stomach. And lately he hasn't been eating his noodles for lunch.

NOGUCHI: That's another record. I've never seen him eat

anything else.

SAKEI: I wonder who the new Chief will be.

TOYO: What's the hurry? You have a long way to go.

Cut to a long shot of ONO *and* SAITO. *They have heard* TOYO'S *remark and look up, startled.* ONO *is assistant chief.*

Cut to WATANABE'S *empty desk. Cut to* WATANABE *walking down a hospital corridor.*

Dissolve to WATANABE *at the hospital drinking-fountain, in the waiting-room.* WATANABE *is trying to get a drink of water; but a man gets there before him.* WATANABE *waits, then drinks and then looks at himself in the mirror.*

Cut to WATANABE *sitting down. Another* MAN *a few chairs away comes and sits next to him.*

MAN: Stomach trouble, eh? Me, I've got something chronic. Lately it's got so that I just don't feel right unless my stomach hurts.

A NURSE *calls his name and the man, the same one that drank before* WATANABE *did, gets up and goes into the office.*

MAN: Now, that fellow there. They say it's ulcers but I think it's cancer. And having cancer is the same as having a death sentence. But the doctors here always tell you it's ulcers, that an operation's unnecessary. They tell you to go on and eat anything — and when you hear that, you know you've got a year left, at the most. Your stomach always feels heavy, and it hurts; you belch a lot and you're always thirsty; either you're constipated or else you have diarrhoea, and in either case your stool is always black.

WATANABE *is feeling more and more uncomfortable. Quiet sinister music. He changes seats but the* MAN *follows him.*

Shot of WATANABE *becoming more and more uncomfortable.*

MAN: And you won't be able to eat meat, or anything you

really like, then you'll vomit up something you ate a week ago; and when that happens, you have about three months left to live.

Cut to a long shot of WATANABE *alone in the waiting-room. The slow and melancholy music of the opening is heard. He is small in the distance, almost lost in the large waiting-room. A* NURSE *suddenly calls his name; she calls it several times because he does not hear. He finally hears, and rises. The music fades. Cut to the X-ray room, two* DOCTORS *and a* NURSE *are waiting. Cut to* WATANABE *entering, then a shot of their faces as they wait for him to sit down. Quick close-up of the* DOCTOR'S *face, then* WATANABE'S.

DOCTOR: Yes, please sit down. Well, it looks as though you have a light case of ulcers.

Cut to WATANABE'S *hands. He drops the coat he is carrying. The music begins again. Cut to their faces.*

WATANABE: Be honest with me. Tell me the truth. Tell me it's cancer.

The DOCTORS' *faces; the* NURSE'S *face; the back of the young* DOCTOR'S *head — he is looking at the X-ray picture. She picks up* WATANABE'S *coat.*

DOCTOR: Not at all. It's just a light case of ulcers, as I said.

WATANABE: Is an operation impossible?

DOCTOR: It's unnecessary. Medicine will fix you up.

WATANABE: But what shall I eat?

DOCTOR: Anything you like, so long as it's digestible.

Cut to WATANABE. *Hearing this he lowers his head so that it almost touches the desk.*

Wipe back to the DOCTORS.

YOUNGER DOCTOR: Will he last a year?

ELDER DOCTOR: No. Six months at the most. What would you do if you only had half a year to live? Miss Aihara, what would you do?

NURSE: Well, there's some poison there on the shelf.

The YOUNGER DOCTOR *turns back to look at the X-ray negative. Close-up of the negative, the sound of the buzzing of the X-ray machine is heard.*

Cut to the street: trucks, cars, WATANABE *walking, but all without sound. When he tries to cross the street, a truck races past, and there is a sudden burst of sound. The traffic streams in front of* WATANABE *and he, small, on the opposite side of the street, cannot cross.*

Wipe to the front of WATANABE'S *house at night. The camera slowly moves towards the front door. The sound of walking and of someone humming the song* 'Too Young,' *then the voices of* WATANABE'S *son,* MITSUO, *and his daughter-in-law,* KAZUE.

KAZUE: There's no lights on — power gone off again, I wonder?

MITSUO: No, the neighbour's lights are on.

KAZUE: That's funny. Is your father out, I wonder? Where's the key?

MITSUO: It's in your bag.

The camera has moved towards the door. Cut from an extreme close-up of part of the door to the hallway from the inside. The two of them open the door and come in.

KAZUE: It was open. Did that maid forget to lock up? Really, that woman forgets everything.

MITSUO: She lives so far away, that's why. It takes her so long to get home that she forgets about everything else.

KAZUE: It wouldn't cost that much more to have her live in.

MITSUO: You know father. He'd never hear of it. Always the minor official.

Cut to the corner of the hallway. They are moving through the dark to the bottom of the stairs.

KAZUE: It's just as cold inside as it is outside — that's what's wrong with Japanese houses.

MITSUO: I always hate coming home. It would be nice to

have a modern house.

Cut to the two of them on the stairs in the dark.

KAZUE: Well, we could build one for about five hundred thousand yen, couldn't we? Though we might have to use your father's retirement pay.

MITSUO: He'll get about seven hundred thousand, and a monthly pension too. And he's got about a hundred thousand saved up.

KAZUE: But do you think he'll agree?

Cut to the darkened upstairs rooms.

MITSUO: Well, he'll just have to live by himself if he doesn't. That will probably be the most effective way. After all, he can't take his money with him. KAZUE *laughs.*

MITSUO *finds the light and turns it on.* WATANABE *is at his feet, he has been sitting there in the dark. Cut to* WATANABE'S *face, then cut to his son's.*

MITSUO: Father, what's the matter?

WATANABE *in despair*: Oh, nothing; nothing at all.

He stands up, confused, then goes downstairs to his own room. Cut to MITSUO *and his wife looking at each other. She begins to turn on more lights.*

KAZUE: But he heard everything we said. Really, that was very rude of him. And he shouldn't have come up here, not while we were away. I call that very impolite.

MITSUO: Why didn't he say what he wanted to? Why did he run away like that?

Cut to WATANABE *in his darkened room downstairs. He turns on the light. Pan with him as he goes to a small shrine in the corner of the room and opens it. Cut to* MITSUO *upstairs; he is lying on the bed, and* KAZUE *is making him move to take off the bedspread. He looks at her, and she comes and sits on the bed. She then lies down beside him.*

KAZUE: Don't look like that. Let's just forget about your father and think a little more about us.

They have turned on the radio and from it comes 'Too Young'. *She turns towards him, hugs him and tells him to hold her.*

Cut to WATANABE'S *room. He is sitting before the open shrine. Cut to the small shrine and to the photograph of his dead wife inside it. Close-up of the picture. Close-up of* WATANABE *looking at it. Big close-up of the picture. Dissolve to a motor-hearse, seen through the rain-flecked windscreen of a following car. The sound of windscreen wipers. Cut to the back seat:* WATANABE, KIICHI, *his brother,* TATSU, *his sister-in-law (all much younger), and* MITSUO, *as a child, are going to a funeral.*

TATSU: And she was so young, too — oh, but it must have been hard for her to leave her little boy behind.

KIICHI: Stop crying.

Cut to the hearse ahead, turning a corner. Cut to the little boy, MITSUO. *Cut to the hearse again, then back to* MITSUO; *the melancholy music of the opening is heard. (The hearse is always seen through the windscreen, its image cut by the wipers.)*

MITSUO: We have to hurry. Mother is leaving us behind.

Cut to the back seat. WATANABE *is holding his son, tears in his eyes.*

Cut back to WATANABE'S *room. From above comes the sound of the song as well as* MITSUO *and* KAZUE'S *muffled laughter. He looks up to where the sound is coming from. They seem to be making love.*

Cut to another room, where WATANABE *and* KIICHI, *his brother, are talking. Both men are much younger.*

KIICHI: You say you can't get married again because of Mitsuo, but just wait. When he grows up he's not going to be all that grateful; after he gets married himself you'll just be in the way. And that is why you ought to get married again now. My wife says that you're naturally sloppy and she says she can't stand the idea of you living all alone and getting more that way.

WATANABE *has been absently turning the pages of a book while his brother has been talking. Now, however, he hears his son calling him.*

Cut back to his room. Again he hears the voice, stands up, walks to the stairs, and starts going up them.

Cut from the top of the stairs. WATANABE *is halfway up when* MITSUO'S *voice continues off.*

MITSUO *off* : Goodnight. And lock up, will you?

WATANABE *stops, then rests his head against a step, then starts back down into the darkness whispering* 'Mitsuo'.

Cut to the hallway. He slowly crosses it and locks the front door. Then from a corner he takes a baseball bat and jams it tight, as is apparently his habit, against one of the sliding doors so that it cannot be opened from the outside.

Cut to a close-up of the baseball bat; at the same time, the sound of a ball being hit; the roar of a crowd; the opening music, soft under the sound of the crowd.

Cut to WATANABE *excitedly watching a baseball game. He turns to the* MAN *next to him.*

WATANABE : Mitsuo! Wasn't that a wonderful hit? See that? That batter is my —

Cut to the baseball game, flashpan of the young MITSUO *running to the home plate. Cut to* WATANABE *who again shouts his son's name. Flashpan to the ball game. Something has gone wrong. Cut to* WATANABE *and the* MAN.

MAN : What's that guy think he's doing anyway?

Cut to WATANABE *in his room, sitting down, the camera descending with him. Cut to* WATANABE *at the ball game, sitting down, the camera descending with him. Cut to* WATANABE *and* MITSUO, *the latter on a stretcher, in a hospital elevator going up, the camera ascending with them.*

WATANABE: You be brave now, Mitsuo; after all, a little appendix operation isn't anything at all.
MITSUO: But, aren't you going to stay?
WATANABE: I . . . I have some things to do.

The elevator door opens and the boy is wheeled out. WATANABE'S *voice is heard repeating his son's name over and over again, as throughout the following scenes, the music rises.*

Cut to the hallway. He is still standing there, repeating his son's name to himself.

Cut to a railway station. It is wartime; the students have been mobilized and are being sent off. Hundreds of people are there: fathers, mothers, brothers, sisters, all waving flags and throwing streamers.

Cut to MITSUO, *now older, in his uniform. He is looking at his father, he calls his name and is very near to tears; he steps down from the train. The train starts; his father pushes him back onto it; he turns towards his father, searching for his face as the train pulls away. All of this time the voice of* WATANABE *can be heard calling over,* 'Mitsuo, Mitsuo, Mitsuo'.

Long dissolve from the boy's face to WATANABE *in the hall. He starts to go up the stairs, but stops halfway. Dissolve to his room. He hangs up his kimono; puts his trousers under the pallet to press them, winds his pocket watch and puts it on the table, reaches for the alarm clock and begins to wind, then drops it. All of this is obviously done by force of habit. Then he suddenly stops. He does not move; the seconds pass; then, without warning, he turns and crawls under the covers. He seems afraid and pulls the covers over his head. He begins to weep.*

A wide shot of the room. Over the huddled WATANABE *are two framed letters on the wall. Cut to a close-up of one of them which reads:*

'LETTER OF COMMENDATION. MR. KANJI WATANABE IS HEREBY GIVEN RECOGNITION FOR HIS TWENTY-FIVE YEARS OF DEVOTED SERVICE.'

The sound of weeping continues.

Cut to the hallway of the house. It is daytime. SAKEI, *the clerk in* WATANABE'S *office, is at the door talking to the maid.*

MAID: But he always leaves for work at the same time.

SAKEI: Huh? He hasn't been to the office for five days, hasn't even sent in an absence report. I was told to come and see what had happened.

She goes into the house to call KAZUE.

Wipe to a telephone box. KAZUE *is inside talking.*

Cut to an office. MITSUO *is on the telephone and we hear their conversation.*

MITSUO: I can't believe it.

KAZUE: But it must be true, that man from his office said so.

MITSUO: But what could he be doing?

Cut to WATANABE'S *office. The others are talking; long shot of his empty desk.*

SAKEI: It's true, and his family was really surprised.

TOYO: But this is awful.

ONO: Well, I can make all the decisions, of course, so long as he's not here.

TOYO: But you have to go and get his seal so that I can leave.

ONO: You mean you're resigning?

Cut to a close-up of TOYO.

TOYO: Yes — this work doesn't suit me.

Wipe to KIICHI'S *house.* MITSUO *is there. They are eating dinner.*

MITSUO: And he's taken fifty thousand yen out of the bank, too.

KIICHI: You don't say . . . Well, maybe he's found himself

a girl. Good for him if he has.
TATSU : Now, now . . .
MITSUO : But that's impossible.
KIICHI : Not at all. It's men like him who fall the hardest. Look, he's been a widower for some twenty years now. And he did it all for you, too. Now he can't stand it any longer and so he goes out and finds someone for himself.
MITSUO : That's nonsense — why, he doesn't look well at all. He's so thin, and his skin's got so dry. Have you seen him recently?
TATSU : Yes, about four days ago. One morning he came over, seemed to want to talk about something. But you know how my husband is. He just looked at him and asked if he'd come for a loan.
KIICHI : I didn't think then that he'd come wanting to talk about some woman, not looking like that.
TATSU : Now, now. My husband, you see, thinks that all men are as bad as he is. Still, Mitsuo, are you certain that something didn't happen over at your house?
MITSUO : No, not that I know of.

But he is evasive and will not look at his aunt and uncle. Cut to a railway crossing. It is evening, almost dark. Cut to a black dog, hunting for food in the dark. Cut to a small drinking stall. Inside a man is at a table writing. He finishes a page and turns to the STALL-KEEPER.

WRITER : Would you take this over to my house? And on the way back get me some sleeping tablets.
KEEPER : But the chemist's closed.
WRITER : Is it that late?
KEEPER : The shops close early round here.
WRITER : If I don't have those pills with my whisky, I just don't sleep.

He hands the page to the STALL-KEEPER, *crumpling the rest of the manuscript in his hand.*

Cut to WATANABE *over in a dark corner; he is hardly visible. He gets up and comes over towards the* WRITER.

WATANABE: Excuse me, but I can let you have some.

He puts the bottle of pills on the counter in front of the WRITER, *then goes back to his table. The* STALL-KEEPER *goes out and the black dog lopes in.*

WRITER: Thanks, may I have them at the official price?

WATANABE: Oh, I was planning to throw them away anyway.

WRITER: Then let me pay for your drinks. You're a heavy drinker, aren't you? Here, let me give you a bit more.

WATANABE: No, I can't . . . I'd just throw it all up. I have gastric cancer.

WRITER *concerned*: Cancer?

WATANABE: Yes.

WRITER: Then you shouldn't drink like this.

He puts his hand on WATANABE'S *shoulder.*

WATANABE: I don't really want to talk about it . . .

WRITER: But to drink, knowing that you have cancer . . . it's like committing suicide.

Cut to the WRITER *looking at him; cut to* WATANABE.

WATANABE: No, it's not that easy. I'd thought of ending it all, but it's hard to die. And I can't die just yet. I don't know what I've been living for all these years.

Cut to the WRITER.

WRITER: Do you have any children? *He receives no answer.* Well, does your stomach hurt?

Cut to WATANABE.

WATANABE: More than my stomach, it's . . . *He presses his chest.*

WRITER: But there must be some reason for all of this.

A shot of both of them.

WATANABE: No, I'm just a stupid fool, that's all. *He pours himself a cup of saké and drinks it.* I'm . . . well, I'm angry with myself. Up until a few days ago I'd never spent anything on drinking. It was only after I found that I didn't have much longer to live that I . . . *He pours himself another cup of saké.*

WRITER: I understand, but you still shouldn't drink. Does it taste good?

WATANABE: No, it doesn't. *He puts down his cup.* But it makes me forget. I'm drinking this expensive saké now because . . . well, because I never did before. It's like drinking poison. I mean, it seems like poison, yet it's so soothing. *He smiles.*

WRITER: I know what you mean.

There is some food on the table which WATANABE *has not eaten. He sees the dog, drops the food on the floor, and the dog bolts it down. Cut back to the two men.*

WATANABE: I have about fifty thousand yen with me. I'd like to spend it having a really good time. But, and I'm ashamed to admit it, I don't know how to. If you would . . .

WRITER: Are you asking me how to spend it, to show you how?

A train passes very near, shaking the stall and making the bottles rattle.

WATANABE: Yes, that is what I wanted to ask you to do.

WRITER: But —

WATANABE: It took me a long time to save this money, but what I mean is that now I can spend it.

During the following speech, shots intercut between the two men.

WRITER: I understand. Look, keep your money. You'll be my guest tonight. Leave it all to me. *He goes across to another table to get his bottle of whisky; he picks it up and comes back to sit down. He looks at* WATANABE *very closely.* You know, you're very interesting. I know I'm being rude, but you're a very interesting person. I'm only a hack writer, I write trashy novels, but you've made me really think tonight. *He pours himself a glass of whisky.* I see that adversity has its virtues —

man finds truth in misfortune; having cancer has made you want to taste life. *He drinks the whisky.* Man is such a fool. It is always just when he is going to leave it that he discovers how beautiful life can be. And even then, people who realize this are rare. Some die without ever once knowing what life is really like. You're a fine man, you're fighting against death — that's what impresses me. Up until now you've been life's slave but now you're going to be its master. And it is man's duty to enjoy life; it's against nature not to. Man must have a greed for life. We're taught that that's immoral, but it isn't. The greed to live is a virtue. *They have moved to the doorway; the sound of a train passing.* Let's go. Let's find that life you've thrown away. Tonight I'll be your Mephistopheles, but a good one, who won't ask to be paid. *He looks down at his feet.* Look, we even have a black dog!

He kicks at the dog and it yelps; over this is the sound of a celeste.

Cut to a close-up of a pin-ball machine, the ball bouncing to the sound of the celeste.

Cut to the two of them in the pin-ball parlour.

WRITER: See this little silver ball? That is you; that's your life. Oh, this is a marvellous machine, a marvellous machine that frees you from all of life's worries; it's an automatic vendor of dreams.

Medium shot of them playing the pin-ball machine. WATANABE *looks very excited.*

Wipe to the two of them in an enormous beer hall. They are sitting with enormous steins of beer in front of them. The writer is just about to speak when trombones, apparently part of a band, are suddenly extended over WATANABE'S *head as he stands up. Deafening music begins.*

Wipe to the streets; a number of fast pans follow the WRITER *and* WATANABE *through the crowds; shots from behind of blinding neon signs and from behind the grill-*

work of fences; a girl races up and snatches away WATANABE'S *hat; he turns and tries to chase her but the* WRITER *stops him.*

WRITER: No . . . girls are the most predatory of all existing mammals. To get that hat back would cost you more than it's worth. But, anyway, you could buy a dozen new hats if you wanted to. Now we're going to buy you a new hat to say good-bye to your old life with.

Cut to them looking through an open-work screen into a small bar.

Cut to them at the entrance of the bar. Medium close-up of the WRITER *stopping to shape* WATANABE'S *new hat. Shot of them coming into the bar.*

From the record-player can be heard Josephine Baker's recording of 'J'ai Deux Amours'. *The* LANDLADY *and barmen stand smiling. She welcomes them, says it has been a long time, and they sit at the bar.* WATANABE *has his new hat in front of him; when she tries to take it away from him, he, instantly suspicious, grabs it and holds onto it. The* WRITER *laughs; she smiles.*

Camera remains on the LANDLADY, *in medium close-up; the* WRITER *can be seen in the mirror behind her.*

WRITER: What's so funny? This man here has gastric cancer.

LANDLADY: Then he shouldn't be drinking, should he?

WRITER: Stupid — no, take a good look at him. See, he's God and he's carrying this cross called cancer. Most people just die the minute they learn this, but not him; he's different. From that moment on he started to live.

She smiles again and the camera turns from them and pans over their glasses to the mirror behind the bar. WATANABE *has put his hat back on, but his head is resting against the bar.*

WRITER: Isn't that right?

WATANABE *slowly raises his head, looks at himself in the mirror, and suddenly smiles.*

Wipe to a big glass-and-neon cabaret. The camera pans down the great stairwell, up which the WRITER *and* WATANABE *are coming, forcing their way through the crowd. A couple is dancing on the landing, very close together.* WATANABE *cannot tear himself away from the sight; the* WRITER *pulls him on.*

Cut to the top floor. Cut to a close-up of piano hammers playing Boogie-Woogie music; a beer-drinking PIANO PLAYER, *a dancing* GIRL; *she takes* WATANABE'S *hat, puts it on, dances around the room. Close-ups of the piano keys; of the huge mirror which hangs above the piano; of the* GIRL *dancing; of* WATANABE *following her around the room; of the* PIANO PLAYER, *smiling from behind the swinging bead-curtain.* WATANABE *finally gets his hat back; the* GIRL *goes off dancing, falls against the keys of the piano, and the* PIANO PLAYER *turns.*

PIANO PLAYER: You folks got any requests?

The GIRL *comes over and sits on* WATANABE'S *lap.*

WATANABE: 'Life Is So Short.'

PIANO PLAYER: I beg your pardon . . .?

WATANABE: 'Life Is So Short.' *He begins to sing.* 'Fall in love, dear maiden . . .'

PIANO PLAYER: Oh, that one — it's an oldie, isn't it? Okay.

He rattles off an introduction, and then pours beer down his throat; couples collect on the dance floor. Cut to the dance floor as seen through the swinging bead-curtain. As it sways back and forth, the couples one by one stop dancing, turning to look. Cut to the GIRL, *she is moving slowly away from* WATANABE'S *chair. The camera circles, in close-up, staying on* WATANABE *as he sings.*

WATANABE: Life is so short,
Fall in love, dear maiden,
While your lips are still red;
Before you can no longer love —

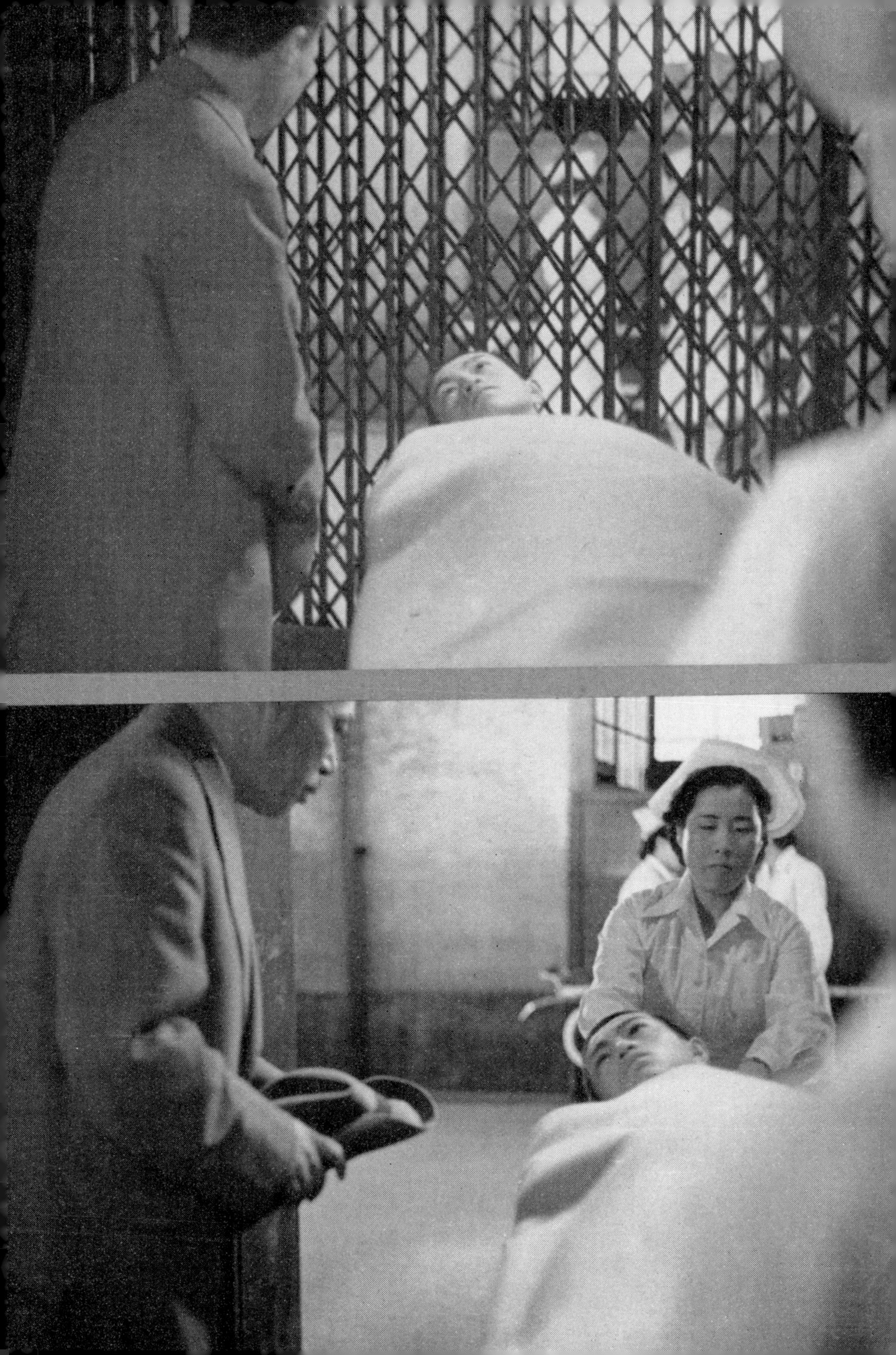

58
56

榎町

For there will be no tomorrow.

Life is so short,
Fall in love, dear maiden,
While your hair is still black,
Before your heart stops —
For there will be no more tomorrow.

Tears stream down WATANABE'S *face. There is silence. Suddenly the* WRITER *stands up, springing into the frame.*

WRITER: That's the spirit!

He takes WATANABE'S *arm, pulling him out of the dance hall. Cut to a strip-show, a woman dancing on a lighted platform, slow, seductive music, the camera panning around her. Cut to her feet as a garment drops. The camera moves towards the* WRITER *and* WATANABE, *both looking at the girl above them. They are both drunk.*

WRITER: That's not art. A strip-tease isn't art. It's too direct. It's more direct than art. That woman's body up there. It's a big, juicy steak; it's a glass of gin, a shot of camphor; it's hormone extract, streptomycin, uranium . . . WATANABE *gulps.*

Wipe to the streets. Both are very drunk. WATANABE *starts across the road, and is almost run over, but the car stops in time.* WATANABE *takes off his coat as though he too were doing a strip-tease. He stops the traffic. The* WRITER *comes and pulls him out of the road.*

Wipe to an enormous dance hall: a great crush of people struggling on the dance floor, cigarette smoke rising from the pack. The band is playing a mambo. Cut as each section of the band strikes up: trumpeters, trombonists, percussionists, standing against the massed dancers.

Cut to WATANABE *in the crowd, dancing with a girl who is chewing gum. She is merely discomfited by the crush; he is nearly frantic. The* WRITER *is almost asleep on his feet; his girl pinches him; he opens his eyes and yawns.*

Cut to a speeding car, the camera travelling alongside it, reflections sliding over the surface. Inside are WATANABE, *the* WRITER, *and the two girls. The reflections slide over the window, past* WATANABE'S *face. He looks very ill. One of the girls is putting on lipstick; then she carefully removes her eyelashes. The other is counting a great roll of money.* WATANABE *looks at them, then out of the window.*

WATANABE : Stop the car!

GIRL : Stop the car! . . . Stop the car!

The car stops. WATANABE *opens the door and runs into the shadows. The girls look irritated.*

WRITER *waking up* : What's the matter, have we got a flat?

GIRL : No, it's your friend; he's probably throwing up.

The WRITER *gets out of the car.* WATANABE *is slowly coming out of the shadows. In the distance over a loud-speaker, comes the sound of a mambo. There is the noise of a train.* WATANABE *smiles — or tries to. He and the* WRITER *look at each other — perhaps* WATANABE *is remembering what he heard in the hospital, that when you begin to vomit you only have three more months to live. Both men are now completely sober. They get back into the car; the car starts.*

GIRL : What are you so gloomy about? I hate gloomy people. Come on, let's sing something nice and gay.

The girls start singing as loudly as they can; WATANABE *and the* WRITER *stare straight ahead.*

GIRL: Come on'a my house, come on'a my house.
I'm a'gonna give you everything.
I'm a'gonna give you a Christmas tree.

Dissolve to a street near WATANABE'S *house. It is day, he is on his way home, still wearing his new hat. Cut to a close-up of the hat, the camera then panning down to his face.*

TOYO *off* : Mr. Watanabe!

Cut to the street. Toyo, *the office girl, is running up behind him. He turns and she catches up with him.*

Toyo: Your new hat almost fooled me. *He takes off his new hat.* I was just looking for your house. Are you going to work?

Watanabe: No.

Toyo: Do you have your seal?

Watanabe: No, it's at home.

Toyo: I want to leave — and I have this new job so I'm sort of in a hurry.

Watanabe: Come home with me, then.

Cut to them walking side by side.

Watanabe: Why are you leaving?

Toyo: The work is so boring. Nothing ever happens in that office. I've stood it for a year and a half now. The fact that you've not been here . . . *She looks at his hat* . . . and your new hat — that's all that's happened in a whole year and a half.

Cut to the upstairs room of Watanabe's *house.* Mitsuo *is tying his tie; his wife is standing next to him.*

Mitsuo: Anyway, just don't say anything to him.

Kazue: I've nothing to say to him.

Mitsuo: Now, don't act like that. After all, it's your fault. If you hadn't started talking about his retirement pay . . .

Kazue: Why blame everything on me? You were the one, if you remember, that started talking about money that night. He can't take his money with him, you said.

Mitsuo: It's funny though. Just because of that . . . he wouldn't start acting like this, just because of that. And he's always come home before. Last night was the first time he's ever stayed out all night.

Kazue: Well, let's not talk about it any more — we don't know what's wrong.

At that moment they hear something. Kazue *runs towards the stairs.*

Cut to the hall. Toyo *and* Watanabe *are going into his*

room. The MAID *takes his hat and stands looking at it. Cut to his room.* TOYO *takes his coat and puts it on a hanger. He is watching her, then turns to his desk. She walks towards him and puts her letter on his desk. As she walks around the room, she sees the framed letter of commendation on the wall.*

TOYO: Almost thirty years in that place, think of it. It gives me the willies. *She glances sideways at him.* I'm sorry.

WATANABE: That's all right. You know, lately, when I look at that letter, well, I remember that joke you read out loud in the office once. It was a very true joke. I've been there almost thirty years and now I can't remember one day, can't remember one thing I did. All I know is that I was always busy and always bored.

He bows his head. She looks at him, then she begins to laugh. Finally, he joins her.

TOYO: That's the first time I've ever heard you talk like that. I didn't even know you could feel like that, I really didn't.

She laughs and impulsively stretches out her hands, takes his, shakes them. The door behind them opens and the MAID *appears with the tea. She stops dead.*

Cut back to the room upstairs.

MITSUO: Now don't be foolish. I know that uncle said the same thing, but I just can't imagine him being in love with such a young girl . . . *They sit on the bed.*

Cut to WATANABE'S *room. He is at his desk; the girl is kneeling politely some distance away. He looks up at her over his glasses.*

WATANABE: But this is the wrong form.

He looks at her; she looks away; then he takes up his seal and stamps her letter of resignation anyway. He hands it to her; she smiles.

WATANABE: Are you going to the office today?

TOYO: Oh, yes. I have to turn this in.

WATANABE: If you wait a minute I'll make my absence

report out. Would you take it in for me?

TOYO: Why don't you go to work yourself? Everyone in the office is talking about it, they say it's 'that time of life.' Are you really sick? You do look pale.

WATANABE: No, I . . .

TOYO: Where do you go every day when you pretend to be going to work? And don't lie, either. Did you know that Mr. Sakei came here yesterday to check on you? *She suddenly laughs.* But, don't worry. After thirty years you deserve some kind of rest. I'm not going to talk about you the way Mr. Carp did.

WATANABE: Mr. Carp?

TOYO: That's just my name for him — but he is just like a carp, you know. Full of airs, but he doesn't have any backbone at all, and he always acts so superior, too — even with me. Just because he makes two hundred yen a month more than I do. WATANABE *laughs and she stands up, a bit embarrassed.* Well, I'll be going now. *She takes the letters and gets her coat. He looks at her.*

Cut to TOYO. *She has two large holes in her stockings.*

WATANABE: Wait, I'll go with you.

Cut to the upstairs window, from the outside. MITSUO *and his wife are looking out.*

Cut to the front gate, WATANABE *and* TOYO *are coming out, both smiling.*

Cut to the couple in the upstairs window, watching.

Cut to the couple below. She stops him, straightens his tie for him.

Cut to MITSUO *and his wife. She smirks; he looks down, worried.*

Cut to the staircase. The MAID *is on her way up to share the news.*

Cut to the street. WATANABE *and* TOYO *are walking and a waltz tune, played by strings and celeste, can be heard over.*

TOYO: But you're very lucky, living in a nice house like that. Why, at my place we have three families living in two rooms. You have a son, don't you?
WATANABE: Where can I buy some women's stockings?
TOYO: You want to buy some — they ought to be selling them somewhere round here. They're for your son's wife, aren't they? Someone told me she was very pretty.

Wipe to a store. They are just coming out and she is holding a pair of new stockings all wrapped up, and is smiling.

TOYO: I'm so excited. Why, I'd have to go without lunch for three months to buy these. But why did you get them for me?
WATANABE: You had holes in your old ones.
TOYO: But that didn't make *your* feet cold.
WATANABE: I just . . .
TOYO: I didn't mean that. *She turns and smiles.* I appreciate it a lot — very much. I only said that because I felt embarrassed.

Suddenly embarrassed, she walks behind him, then, laughingly, pushes him.

Wipe to a tea parlour. He looks at her, passes her his piece of cake. She smiles and helps herself to sugar, putting in lump after lump.

TOYO: Want me to tell you something? Well, I've given everyone in our office a nickname. It was something to do, so I wouldn't get so bored. Want to hear?
WATANABE: Yes.
TOYO: All right. Now, the first one is — Mr. Sea-Slug. Now, who is that? Someone that's hard to pin down, keeps squirming away. *He does not know. She giggles.* It's Mr. Ono!

WATANABE *smiles, nods.*

WATANABE: Of course.
TOYO: Next is Mr. Drain-Cover. Think, now. Someone who's damp all year round.
WATANABE: Mr. Ohara?

TOYO: That's right! And then there's Mr. Fly-Paper. A very sticky person. Come, you know. You don't? Mr. Noguchi. And do you want to know what I named Mr. Saito? He doesn't have anything special about him and yet he's the same all the time.
WATANABE: Saito? I don't know.
TOYO: Mr. Menu.
WATANABE: Menu?
TOYO: Yes, you know, like in cheap restaurants. The menu is always the same and it's never any good. *They both laugh.*
WATANABE: What about Kimura?
TOYO: I call him Mr. Jello because he's so weak and wobbly. I gave you a nickname too, but I won't say it. I won't because it wouldn't be nice to.
WATANABE: Please do. I wouldn't mind. Anyway, I'd like it if you made it up.
TOYO: All right. It's . . . it's Mr. Mummy. *She starts to laugh, then stops.* I'm sorry.
WATANABE: That's all right. *She begins laughing again, then he starts to laugh too.*

Wipe to outside the shop.

TOYO: Well, thanks for everything.
WATANABE: Do you have to resign today? Can't you put it off until tomorrow? Won't you stay with me today?

Wipe to a pin-ball parlour; he is teaching her how to play and she is enjoying herself. Wipe to an ice-skating rink; she is teaching him how to skate — they both fall down. Wipe to a fun-fair, they are eating noodles and laughing. Wipe to an ice-cream shop; she is eating; he smiles and gives her his portion. Wipe to a cinema; apparently a cartoon is on the screen, because she is laughing and leaning forward in her excitement; he is asleep beside her. Wipe to a Japanese-style restaurant; they are having dinner.

TOYO: But you don't eat at all — and you really do look

exhausted.
WATANABE: No, I really enjoyed myself today.
TOYO: But, you fell asleep in the movie. You were snoring just when the best part came.
WATANABE: Well, last night . . . *He pauses and she laughs.* I can't tell this to anyone, I'm ashamed to admit it, but the reason why I've been like a mummy for the past thirty years . . . *She chokes on a glass of water* . . . Oh, don't misunderstand, I'm not angry you called me a mummy. It's true, and it couldn't be helped, it's just that . . . the reason I turned into a mummy was . . . well, it was all for my son's sake. But now he doesn't appreciate it. He . . .
TOYO: Well, you can't very well blame him for that. *She smooths her new stockings.* He didn't ask you to become a mummy. Parents are all alike — my mother says just the same thing. She says: I have suffered because of you. But, if you think about it, well, I appreciate being born, I really do; but I wasn't responsible for it. *She pauses.* But why are you talking about your son like that to me?
WATANABE: Well, it's just . . .

Close-up of TOYO *breaking into a smile.*

TOYO: I know you love him!

Close-up of WATANABE *smiling.*

Wipe to the street at night, WATANABE *is returning home alone. The sad music of the opening, now sounding even more desperate.*

Wipe to the interior of the house. WATANABE *is sitting, head bowed, at one side of the table; his son is reading the newspaper on the other side; the wife is nearby, knitting.*

MITSUO: It says here that the power shortage will last for a while.
WATANABE: Is that so?

Close-up of WATANABE, *his head lowered, although he seems to want to say something.*

Close-up of the son's newspaper; close-up of the wife, busy with her knitting; close-up of WATANABE *raising his head.*

MITSUO *off*: It says here that this is the warmest winter in thirty years.

WATANABE *does not hear, then realizing that something has been said, he looks up quickly.*

WATANABE: Is that so?

Cut to all three of them. WATANABE *leans forward. His hand shakes as he puts his cup down.*

WATANABE: If you don't mind, I'd like to talk to you for a few minutes. I wanted to tell you earlier, but it isn't a very pleasant story and . . .

MITSUO: I don't want to hear it. *Suddenly puts down the paper.* I've talked the whole problem over with Uncle today, and he thinks that it ought to be disposed of in a business-like way as well. For example, I think that our rights to your property should be made clear.

WATANABE: Mitsuo!

KAZUE *gets up and leaves the room.* MITSUO *leans forward.*

MITSUO: You've already spent over fifty thousand yen on her — girls nowadays!

WATANABE: Mitsuo, what are you . . .?

MITSUO: Father! We never meddle in your affairs. We've shut our eyes to your going out every night and doing I don't know what. I just now made a practical suggestion. But you must consider Kazue and her family's position in this. The idea — bringing a girl here, and holding hands too. I was terribly embarrassed when the housekeeper told me.

WATANABE *stands up. The camera pans with him as he hurries across the room and over to the stairs.*

Fade out. Then fade in to WATANABE'S *office — his chair is vacant. Cut to various scenes of the office workers talking to each other, whispering, smiling, smirking. Someone comes up to* Ono *and whispers.* Ono, *due to be promoted now that* Watanabe *is no longer there, laughs indulgently. Over all of this the voice of the* Narrator *is heard.*

Narrator *off*: The hero of our story has now been absent for about two weeks, and during this time, naturally, various rumours, various surmises have been repeated. All of these came to the single conclusion that Mr. Watanabe had been behaving very foolishly. Yet, to Watanabe, these same actions were the most meaningful of his entire life.

Cut to the window of a toy factory. The machinery hums; the window rattles; the building shakes — toy rabbits are stacked in boxes along the wall. Cut to outside. Toyo *and* Watanabe *are talking. She is wearing a turban round her head and has obviously been working — also, she is angry.*

Toyo: This isn't the City Hall, you know. You can't take a whole day to do one hour's work here. Every second wasted means less money.

Watanabe: Meet me tonight — just tonight.

Toyo: I'm tired at night. I'd rather sleep. Besides, why do you want to go out with me every night? Let's just stop it. It's . . . it's unnatural.

Watanabe: Tonight — only tonight.

Toyo: No. This has to stop. Excuse me.

She turns and runs back into the factory. He walks away. Cut to Watanabe *alone among tables full of white mechanical rabbits. A door opens and she joins him.*

Toyo: All right, but tonight is absolutely the last time.

Wipe to the second floor of a large and fancy coffee shop. Watanabe *comes in and sits at* Toyo's *table. In the rear, on the balcony, is a big group of boys and girls. A record-player is playing Poldini's* ' Waltzing Doll,' *and the boys and girls talk excitedly as a large birthday cake is brought up the stairs.* Toyo *looks at the couple next*

to them, then at the birthday party, then she yawns.
WATANABE *looks at her, leans forward.*

WATANABE: Let's take a walk.

TOYO: No, thank you. After the walk would be the noodle-shop; and after that would be the ice-cream parlour. What's the use? I know I'm being ungrateful, but I'm really bored. We don't have anything to talk about.

Cut to WATANABE, *looking at her. He lowers his head.*

TOYO: That look again . . .

Cut back to her, in close-up.

TOYO: You make me nervous. Why do you pay so much attention to me?

WATANABE: It's because . . .

TOYO: Because why?

WATANABE: Well, I just enjoy being with you.

TOYO: I hope it isn't love.

WATANABE: No, it's not . . .

TOYO: Why don't you speak more clearly — say what you mean!

Cut to WATANABE. *He lowers his eyes.*

TOYO *leaning forward*: Are you angry?

WATANABE: No. I don't know myself . . . *Close-up of him* . . . why I like being with you. All I know is that . . .

Cut to both of them at the table. The record-player begins 'The March of the Wooden Soldiers.'

WATANABE: . . . is that I'm going to die soon. I have gastric cancer.

Cut to a close-up of her.

Cut to a close-up of him — he presses his hand against himself.

WATANABE: In here. You understand? I have less than a year to live. And when I found that out . . . then, somehow, I was drawn to you. Once when I was a little boy I nearly drowned. It is just that feeling. Darkness is everywhere and there is nothing for me to hold on to, no matter how I try.

There is only you.

Close-up of her — she looks very uncomfortable.

TOYO: What about your son?

Cut to a shot of both of them; TOYO *with her back to camera.*

WATANABE: Don't even talk about him. I have no son; I'm all alone.

TOYO: Don't talk like that.

WATANABE: You don't understand. My son is somewhere far away, just as my parents were far away when I was drowning. I can't bear to think about it.

TOYO: But what help am I?

WATANABE: You . . . well, just to look at you makes me feel better. It . . . it warms this . . . *He looks down* . . . this mummy heart of mine. And you are kind to me. No, that's not it. It's because you are so young and healthy. No, it isn't that either. *He rises, comes to her side of the table, sits down; she is repelled, and tries to move further away.* You are so full of life and . . . and I'm envious of that. If only I could be like you for one day before I die. I won't be able to die unless I can be. Oh, I want to do something. Only you can show me. I don't know what to do. I don't know how to do it. Maybe you don't either, but, please, if you can, show me how to be like you.

TOYO: I don't know.

WATANABE: How can I be like you?

TOYO: But all I do is work and eat — that's all.

WATANABE: Really?

TOYO: Really. That and make toys like this one.

She has a toy rabbit in her pocket. She takes it out, winds it up, puts it on the table in front of them; it hops towards him; she picks it up, starts it over again.

TOYO: That's all I do, but it's fun. I feel as if I were friends with all the children in Japan now. Mr. Watanabe, why don't you do something like that, too?

WATANABE : What can I do at the office?

TOYO : That's true. Well then, resign and find some other work.

WATANABE : It's too late.

Cut to her looking at him; then cut to both of them with the mechanical rabbit between them.

WATANABE : No, it's not. It isn't impossible.

A shot of him, with tears in his eyes. She is afraid; she moves back — ' The March of the Wooden Soldiers ' *gets louder. He suddenly turns to her, smiling; she shrinks back.*

WATANABE : I *can* do something if I really want to!

He picks up the rabbit.

Cut to the boys and girls on the balcony, they are leaning over the rail.

BOYS AND GIRLS : Here she comes! Happy birthday to you, happy birthday to you!

WATANABE *hurries past them down the stairs, the rabbit in his hand. The girl, whose birthday it is, comes up the stairs, smiling, while the others continue ot sing* ' Happy Birthday.'

Cut to TOYO, *sitting alone. The birthday party is noisy and happy but she does not turn to look, she stares straight ahead.*

Fade out.

Then fade in to the Citizens' Section. ONO *is coming into the office, followed by* SAITO, *the camera panning with them.*

ONO : Oh, he'll resign soon enough — his son was here asking about his retirement pay.

SAITO : Well, then you'll be our new chief, won't you?

ONO *smiles, satisfied, yet trying to appear modest.*

ONO : It's difficult to tell just yet.

He is about to hang up his coat, when they both see WATANABE'S *new hat hanging there, they look towards his desk. Cut to the desk.* WATANABE *is hunting for something, finds it and sits down.* ONO *and* SAITO *look amazed. They walk towards* WATANABE'S *desk. He looks up at them.*

WATANABE : Here, Ono, take care of this.

He hands him a document on which is written: 'PETITION FOR RECLAIMING DRAINAGE AREA — KUROE-CHO WOMEN'S ASSOCIATION.' There is a notice attached which says: 'This Petition is to be forwarded to the Public Works Section.' WATANABE *tears off the notice.*

ONO : But this petition should go —

WATANABE : No, unless we do something about it, nothing will ever be done. Everyone will have to co-operate, the Public Works Section, the Parks Section, the Sewage Section — all must co-operate. Now call me a car. I must make an inspection, and prepare a report today.

ONO : But this will be difficult.

WATANABE : No, it won't, not if you are determined.

The camera pans with WATANABE *as he hurries to put on his coat. The noon siren is heard.* ONO *hurries to follow but* WATANABE *is already out of the door.*

Cut to outside where a light rain is falling. The door swings to and ONO *follows, worried. The sound of trumpets playing the final cadence of* 'Happy Birthday' *can be heard over.*

NARRATOR *off* : Five months later, the hero of this story died.

A picture of WATANABE *on the funeral altar.*

Cut to the entire altar. It is in WATANABE'S *room, which is now almost unrecognizable in its funeral trappings. Everything is still and there is very little movement. The entire office staff is there, as well as the* DEPUTY MAYOR, *and all* WATANABE'S *family. They are kneeling on cushions laid out on either side of the altar. Cut to outside the window, looking in. They are drinking saké.*

The sound of a car driving up and stopping. Cut to the DEPUTY MAYOR *listening.* MITSUO'S *wife gets up and goes to the hallway. Cut to the hallway. A group of reporters has gathered there.*

REPORTER: We'd like to see the Deputy Mayor, please, just for a few minutes.

Cut to the funeral room. ONO *comes in and whispers to the* MAYOR.

ONO: Sir, those reporters . . .

Cut to the MAYOR *politely leaving the room. Cut to the hall.*

MAYOR: Now just what's the idea —my conscience is clear.

REPORTER: Are you sure? We've been finding out a few things.

2ND REPORTER: And though both you and the Parks Section are claiming all the credit, wasn't it really this Watanabe who made the park?

MAYOR: He was Chief of the Citizens' Section; parks fall under the Parks Section.

2ND REPORTER: We know that, but what we want to know is who did all the work? The people around there all think it was this Watanabe, and they think it funny that he died there.

MAYOR: What do you mean?

3RD REPORTER: They think something funny is going on. For example, in your opening speech you didn't even mention Watanabe. The people there say that this wasn't right.

MAYOR: If it wasn't, what would have been then?

2ND REPORTER: Maybe it was a political speech.

The MAYOR *tries to laugh. Just then a flashbulb goes off. His picture has been taken. He is disconcerted.*

3RD REPORTER: And Watanabe was given a seat way in the back and was ignored. These people think that his dying like that in the park means something.

MAYOR: Do they mean that he committed suicide in the park? Deliberately sat there and froze to death?

3RD REPORTER: Yes.
MAYOR: Things like that happen in plays and novels. We happen to know what killed Watanabe. It was gastric cancer.
2ND REPORTER: Cancer?
MAYOR: Yes, an internal haemorrhage. He died quite suddenly and he didn't know that he was going to. If you doubt me, Mr. Ono here will . . . *He indicates* ONO *who is now standing beside him* . . . Give them the name of the hospital that made the autopsy.

Cut to the MAYOR *politely coming back into the room and sitting down. The sound of an automobile going away, dying in the distance.* ONO *returns and sits down. There is a silence; everyone feels rather uncomfortable. The* DEPUTY MAYOR *takes a cup of saké.*

MAYOR: The way that these reporters twist the facts. *He drinks his saké, then turns to the others around him.* It's not nice to say, but they truly fail to understand the problems behind municipal projects. *They all bow, nod, smiling, agreeing.* They simply don't understand organization. Now, that park, for example. They seem to think that Mr. Watanabe built it all by himself. But that is just silly. It is probably rude of me to say this in front of his relatives, but I'm certain that Mr. Watanabe didn't have this in mind — building a park all by himself. Of course, he worked very hard towards helping and, I must admit, I was impressed by his perseverance. But it was the work of the section too. *All the section clerks nod in agreement.* And, in any event, it is complete nonsense for anyone who knows anything about the organization to say that the Chief of the Citizens' Section could go and build a park all by himself. *Everyone nods.* I'm sure that the deceased himself would be amused. *Everyone laughs.* But, then, none of us are exactly faultless, and in view of what I said at that time, perhaps we should have given more recognition to those truly responsible, since the park has now drawn so much attention. For example, the Chief of Parks . . . *That gentleman*

bows . . . and his superior, the Chief of Public Works. *That gentleman also bows.*

PUBLIC WORKS CHIEF: It is good of you to say that, Sir, but it is my belief that the Chief of the Parks Section and myself only pushed the plan, insofar as paper work was concerned. When I think of his honour's painstaking efforts to bring this plan to materialization, then I know that it is the Deputy Mayor himself who should be rewarded. *Everyone smiles and nods at this.*

MAYOR: No, I've been criticized — criticized even for that speech at the opening of the park. One of them called it a political speech, didn't he, Ono?

He is about to say more when the HOUSEKEEPER *comes in and tells* MITSUO'S *wife that some women from Kuroe-Cho have come to pay their respects.*

A group of women, many of the same who came to the Citizens' Section before, now enter the room. They do not wait to be invited, but walk directly to the altar. Many are crying. They bow before the picture; they light incense. A baby on the back of one of them starts to cry.

Cut to MITSUO, *looking at them.*

Cut to his wife. It is not proper for her to remain standing in the middle of the room and so she kneels.

Cut to a view of the entire room. The officials are embarrassed and frowning; only one of them, KIMURA, *is affected; he puts his hands to his eyes as though to hide tears. Then the women get up to leave the room. As the women go, they bow to the other guests and only one,* KIMURA, *bows in return. There is a long silence.*

Cut to WATANABE'S *picture; cut to a closer shot; cut to one even closer — the grain of the photograph is visible.*

Cut to a view of the entire room. The wife, who has seen the women out, returns and sits down. The silence continues unbroken.

Then the DEPUTY MAYOR *nods to the* CHIEF OF PUBLIC

WORKS *and the* CHIEF OF PARKS. *They kneel, bow to the shrine and altar, bow to the family, then politely and carefully take their leave.* ONO, *who has gone to see them out, returns.*

ONO : It's cold, isn't it?

KIICHI : Have a drink. *He holds out a saké bottle.* Oh, I'm sorry. This saké is cold, I'll go and get some warm. How about everyone getting together, sitting a little closer together?

There is a general movement, almost a scramble. ONO *successfully gets the seat just vacated by the* MAYOR. *Others must be content with lesser positions. Old* OHARA *stands up too late, looks for a seat on the other side; all are taken; he sits down, grumbling. Someone asks if they had gone off to their conference.*

KIMURA : Yes, they couldn't bear it here any longer. Mr. Watanabe built that park, no matter what anyone says. And the Mayor knows it. That's why he . . .

ONO : Now, you're going too far. Mr. Watanabe just . .

CLERK : It's not just because I'm in the Parks Section, but I know that our section planned and carried out the whole thing.

KIMURA : That's not what I mean.

SAITO : That's all right. We know how you feel, but why should the Chief of the Citizens' Section try to build a park anyway? It is outside his . . . his sphere of influence.

NOGUCHI : Anyway, no one built that park. It was just a coincidence. And no councillor would have done anything about it anyway, if it hadn't been that elections are coming up. KIMURA *is about to say something but* NOGUCHI *continues.* And if it hadn't been for all the graft, come to think of it, work might not have gone so smoothly either.

OHARA : I just can't understand it. *He shakes his head, talking as though to himself.* Why should Mr. Watanable change so — he changed so suddenly.

ONO : Yes, it was strange.

SAITO : That's it. Now that I think of it . . . Mr. Watanabe knew about his cancer. That's why.

Cut to Ono *as he turns to* Mitsuo, *who has just returned with more saké.*

Ono : We were just speaking of your father — did he know he had gastric cancer?

Mitsuo : If he had, he would certainly have told me. I think that father was very fortunate in knowing nothing about it. After all, to learn something like that is just like getting a death sentence.

Kiichi *comes back into the room.*

Ono : Then Saito's theory is wrong.

Kiichi : What's that?

Ono : Mr. Watanabe changed so in the last five months, and we can't understand why.

Kiichi : Oh, that. It was because of a woman. You know, often an older man tries to hold onto his youth by keeping a mistress. His complexion gets better, his eyes get brighter . . . *His wife is looking at him* . . . Anyway, I think he was keeping some woman.

Ono : Well, he did take to wearing a rather elegant hat.

There are smiles and nods at this. Saito *turns and looks at the picture of* Watanabe *on the altar.*

Saito : That hat. It really surprised me.

Cut to the conclusion of the former scene where Watanabe *has handed the report to* Ono. *The dialogue is as before.*

Ono : But this will be difficult.

Watanabe : No, it won't, not if you are determined.

The camera pans with Watanabe *as he hurries to put on his coat. The noon siren is heard.*

Ono : But —

Cut to a vacant lot in Kuroe-Cho; it is raining. Watanabe *walks round in the rain, through mud, looking at where the playground will be. One of the women runs up to him carrying an umbrella, holding it over him.*

Cut back to the funeral room.

SAITO : He seemed to be trying so hard. It just wasn't natural.

ONO : Well, that's true. Yet, you know, it is hard to believe, that just the influence of a woman could have . . .

KIICHI : But . . .

TATSU : Don't.

OHARA : I just can't understand it.

PARKS CLERK : Well, there was a time when Mr. Watanabe's effort made things very difficult.

SEWAGE SECTION CLERK : You're right, but what I can't understand is why a man who had been an official for the last thirty years should —

KIMURA : That's because —

PARKS CLERK : And he really shouldn't have gone around trying to talk all the other sections into it like that. Naturally, they didn't like it — my chief in particular. He felt that the parks were all his own responsibility.

Cut to the Section of Parks. WATANABE *is offering a petition. The* CHIEF OF PARKS *turns wearily.*

CHIEF : Now, we have many park projects.

WATANABE : Please. The conditions here are terrible.

CHIEF : But it just isn't as easy as your plan here makes it seem.

Cut to the same location, some time has apparently passed. WATANABE *is sitting to one side; the* CHIEF OF PARKS *is trying to work, but cannot. He keeps glancing at* WATANABE *who is sitting there, his head bowed. Finally, the* CHIEF *takes the petition and, with deliberation, stamps it and puts it in the 'out-going' basket, then turns and looks at* WATANABE *who does not move.*

Cut back to the funeral.

SAITO : Mr. Watanabe just hung on until the Chief finally gave in.

PUBLIC WORKS CLERK: Now that you say so, it was just the same with my boss. That Watanabe, he just wouldn't give in. Why, my chief used to turn and run when he saw him coming.

Cut to a corridor in the City Hall. The CHIEF OF PUBLIC WORKS *sees* WATANABE *coming, turns and hurries away, but it is too late:* WATANABE *has seen him and starts after him.*

Cut to the funeral — most of the men are getting drunk.

SANITATION CLERK: But what surprised me most was the way that he, a big chief like that, acted towards clerks like me.

Cut to the Sanitation Section. WATANABE *is going up to each member of the office and bowing. Each must stand and return his bow. With each bow* WATANABE *murmurs,* 'Please,' *as the embarrassed clerks bow back.*

SANITATION CLERK *off*: And we finally gave in too.

Cut to the funeral.

PUBLIC WORKS CLERK: We all felt sorry for him.

NOGUCHI: But it was you General Affairs Section people that gave him the most trouble.

GENERAL AFFAIRS CLERK: Oh, you think so?

ONO: It's true. I went round with him for almost two weeks. I'll never forget it.

GENERAL AFFAIRS CLERK: I'm sorry, Sir.

SAITO: But what surprised me most was that incident when . . .

SAKEI: Oh, that. That was really surprising.

Cut to the stairway leading past the Citizens' Section. WATANABE *is walking at the head of a number of women, the wives from Kuroe-Cho. He goes directly up the stairs, his own clerks staring at him. In the corridor at the top he takes off his coat, gives it to one of the women to hold, and goes into a door marked 'DEPUTY*

MAYOR'S OFFICE.'

Cut to the funeral.

ONO : And that wasn't all.

SAITO : What happened in the Mayor's office?

ONO : Well, I just doubt that anyone ever stood up to the Mayor like he did.

Cut to the DEPUTY MAYOR'S *Office.* WATANABE *is bowing;* ONO *stands behind him.*

MAYOR : I personally don't mind your pushing this park project like this, but some people might think that you were looking for publicity. The City Council has a lot of problems. It would be best if you'd just forget about it.

This taken care of, he turns back to his friends and continues an apparently interrupted conversation.

MAYOR : And so I attended that party last night, but, really, the geisha nowadays are no good at all. One of them didn't open her mouth all night, and later I heard that she's a geisha only at night, it's a kind of side-line.

FRIEND : How amusing!

WATANABE : Would you . . . please reconsider. WATANABE *has gone on bowing.* ONO *is trying to make him go. The* MAYOR *turns, incredulous; his friends look up.*

MAYOR : What did you say?

Cut to WATANABE. *He is bowing, yet looking the* MAYOR *full in the face.*

WATANABE : About that park. Please . . . reconsider.

Cut to the MAYOR *staring at him.*

Cut back to WATANABE, *staring, and* ONO *trying to pull him away.*

Cut back to the funeral. There is silence, then laughter. Most of the men are now really drunk.

SAITO : Yet, judging from the results, it wasn't such a bad plan.

SAKEI : No, it was dangerous. Just think of all the . . . the spheres of influence at the City Hall.

Cut to KIMURA.

KIMURA: But the Mayor reconsidered, didn't he?

NOGUCHI: Oh, that. It was some councillor's idea. He made him do it. The whole thing was a sort of accident, you see, a kind of coincidence — you're just sentimental, that's all.

There is some laughter at the word 'sentimental.'

SAKEI: Yes, that's it, sentimental.

KIMURA: I don't think so. If you can't try to understand a man like Mr. Watanabe without being thought sentimental, then the world is a dark place indeed.

NOGUCHI: And so it is — very dark.

KIMURA: I don't know what it was that was keeping Mr. Watanabe alive, but sometimes I was almost afraid for him.

Cut to a corridor in the City Hall. KIMURA *has stopped at the top of the stairs and looks at* WATANABE *in the far distance. He is leaning against the wall, with apparently no strength left. Then, very slowly, he pushes himself along the wall in the direction of the* MAYOR'S *office.*

Cut to a close-up of WATANABE.

Cut back to the funeral.

PARK SECTION CLERK: And, come to think of it, there was that day at the park site.

Cut to the park site. Dust, gravel, a leveller. It almost runs over WATANABE. *One of the women hurries up, pulls him back. She and several others take him to one of the houses, offer him a glass of water. He takes it and drinks some water. Cut to a close-up of* WATANABE *looking at the park site.*

PARK SECTION CLERK *off*: When he looked at that park . . . *Cut back to the funeral, the* CLERK *speaking* . . . his face just glowed. It was . . . well, it was like a man looking at his own grandchild.

KIMURA: Naturally, it was just that to him.

ONO: So, that's why . . .

KIMURA: That's why, no matter what anyone says, it was Mr.

Watanabe who built that park.

NOGUCHI: But if the Mayor and the councillors hadn't done anything there wouldn't have been any park. He just didn't take into consideration all of those . . . those spheres of influence up above.

ONO: Oh, I wouldn't say that.

NOGUCHI: No?

ONO: You remember what happened? With that big combine that wanted to put up a cabaret where the park is?

Cut to a corridor. WATANABE *and* ONO *are walking along it. Several men are lounging against the wall. One steps forward, taking off his dark glasses.*

MAN: You chief of the Citizens' Section?

WATANABE: Yes, I am.

MAN: Wanted to see you. Look, mister, just don't poke your nose in any more, okay?

He smiles, flicks WATANABE'S *lapel;* WATANABE *looks at him.*

WATANABE: Why? Who are you?

The MAN *grabs the lapels of* WATANABE'S *coat, tightens his grip.*

MAN: Don't act stupid, I'm telling you, see? You just cut it out and don't do anything dumb any more.

Cut to WATANABE. *He is smiling.*

Cut to the group; the MAN *releases him.* WATANABE *turns to go into the* MAYOR'S *office. Just then another* MAN, *obviously one of them, comes out and looks at* WATANABE.

MAN: This is Watanabe — remember him.

He stares hard at WATANABE, *who smiles back, and then goes into the office. The gang begins to move off.* ONO *stands looking after them. The second* MAN *— the threatening killer — turns and looks at* ONO, *who turns and hurries into the office.*

Cut to the funeral. Everyone is now drunk. Old OHARA

is thinking, his head to one side.

OHARA : But it's strange. I just can't understand why he changed like that — he must have known he had cancer.

ONO *suddenly sits up, drunk, makes a gesture.*

ONO : I just remembered !

Cut to a staircase in the City Hall. ONO *is obviously lecturing* WATANABE, *who leans, drawn and tired, against the railing.*

ONO : Now, this is too much. You've been doing this for two weeks now. The least they could do is tell you whether they have the money or not. And the way they treat you. At least they could do it nicely — it should make you angry to be insulted this way.

WATANABE : But it doesn't. I don't have time to be angry with anyone. *He goes on down the stairs.*

Cut to the funeral. A general commotion, each person remembering something.

ONO : And then . . .

SAITO : Now that you mention it, I remember once when . . .

Cut to a bridge above the park site. It is sunset. WATANABE *and* SAITO *are walking across it.*

WATANABE : Oh, how beautiful . . . *he looks up* . . . For thirty years I have never watched a sunset. Now there's no more time.

Cut back to the funeral.

SAKEI : It's all clear now . . .

NOGUCHI : He knew he didn't have long to live.

SAITO : That clears everything up, explains everything. Now I understand why he acted that way, it wasn't strange at all, it was normal.

ONO : We'd all do the same thing ourselves.

Cut to KIMURA.

KIMURA : We'll all die ourselves one day.

A general shot of the group. A pause, then OHARA *moves forward.*

OHARA: Look here, Ono. Now, I don't mean that . . . I mean Mr. New Chief of the Citizens' Section, that's what I mean. Look here, can't you hear me?

Cut to ONO, *drunk, pleased, and irritated, all at the same time.*

ONO: I haven't been appointed yet.

OHARA: All right then, Ono, what did you just say? That we'd have done the same thing ourselves? Don't make me laugh. *He drunkenly points to* ONO.

OHARA: You fellows couldn't do what Mr. Watanabe did. Don't make me laugh. Me, I only went to night-school, and that's why I'll never be chief of any Citizens' Section. But, you, Ono, someone like you! Well, just don't make me laugh.

SAITO *tries to stop* OHARA*; then, struck with a sudden thought, stops.*

SAITO: Compared with Mr. Watanabe, all of us are just . . .

OHARA: We're trash, that's what, trash. And you're trash too.

SAKEI: We're all trash. Oh, there are some fine men at the City Hall, but after you've worked there for a long time, it changes you.

NOGUCHI: Yes, that's the place where you don't dare even think. If you do you're dangerous. You must only act as though you're thinking and doing something.

PUBLIC WORKS CLERK: That's right.

GENERAL AFFAIRS CLERK: Yes, that's right.

SAITO: You can't do anything. Why, to get permission for a new trash-can you have to make out enough documents to fill up that trash-can.

SAKEI *moves forward excitedly, then suddenly begins to cry.*

SAKEI: And you have to put your seal on everything: stamp, stamp, stamp!

NOGUCHI: The way we live is by stealing time — people complain about official corruption, but that's nothing compared with our criminal waste of time.

ONO *crawls on all fours into the middle of the room and waves his arms.*

ONO : Listen, fellows! I know how you feel. I think about it too, but what can you do with such a big organization — anyway, there's time to think.

OHARA : You fool! *They all look round at him.*

SAITO : But, look, Ohara. In this organization where you can't do anything, Mr. Watanabe did something, and he did it because he had cancer.

SAKEI : That's just what I wanted to say. *He begins sobbing.*

NOGUCHI : Oh, it makes me mad.

SAKEI : Me, too!

NOGUCHI : And Mr. Watanabe never got any reward at all.

They are all crawling about on the floor.

SAITO : Oh, but when I think of what Mr. Watanabe must have felt . . .

NOGUCHI : Whoever went and took the credit isn't even human.

OHARA : Oh, come out and say it's the Mayor.

NOGUCHI : Now, you be careful what you say.

There is a pause. SAKEI *is crying softly.*

SAKEI : But I just wonder what Mr. Watanabe felt when he was dying out there all alone in the park — just to think of it makes me feel awful.

Most of the men begin to cry now. Among those who do not is KIMURA.

Cut to WATANABE'S *picture on the altar.*

Cut to the doorway. The MAID *appears carrying* WATANABE'S *hat. It is now crushed and dirty.*

MAID : Excuse me, but a policeman just brought this, he found it in the park.

Cut to a close-up of the hat in her hands. Everyone turns to look at it.

MAID : And he said, he wanted to come in and pay his

respects.

Cut. A young policeman comes in, bows, goes to the altar, prays and then gets up to go.

KAZUE : Thank you for coming.

KIICHI : Won't you sit down and have a drink?

He indicates a cushion and pours the POLICEMAN *a cup of saké. The* POLICEMAN *is ill at ease, takes the saké, puts it down. He is apparently deciding whether to speak or not.*

POLICEMAN : I . . . I saw him in the park on that night. It was about ten. No . . . *Looks at his watch* . . . it was closer to eleven, I guess. He was sitting on one of the children's swings. I thought he was probably drunk, but I didn't do anything. If I had, then maybe all of this wouldn't have happened. I am truly sorry. *The* POLICEMAN *bows.*

Cut to MITSUO *looking at the hat which he now holds.*

POLICEMAN : But, he looked so, well, so happy. How can I say it? And he was singing . . . and it was in a voice that, well, moved me.

Cut to the park. In the distance, behind a children's maze, is WATANABE *sitting on a swing; snow is falling. He is singing. The camera pans along the maze, tracking in nearer.*

WATANABE : Life is so short,
Fall in love, dear maiden,
While your lips are still red;
Before you can no longer love —
For there will be no more tomorrow.

Dissolve to WATANABE'S *picture over the altar. The song continues, there is a cut to the funeral; shots of various faces; then of* MITSUO *standing up. Overcome, he goes into the corridor.* KAZUE, *followed by* MITSUO'S *uncle, goes out to him.*

MITSUO : And I found a box with my name on it, on the stairs that night, and in it were his bank book and his seal, and his retirement allowance papers.
KAZUE : He must have left them . . .
MITSUO : But that was bad of him ! If he knew he had cancer, why didn't he tell us? *He begins to cry; his uncle comes forward.*
KIICHI : And his mistress, why didn't she come to the funeral? Maybe there wasn't any mistress.

Cut to a close-up of a packing-case. In it are the framed letters of commendation, an alarm-clock, a white toy rabbit.

Cut back to the funeral. The men are now sitting close together, very drunk, very excited. During the scene KIMURA *leaves them and goes to kneel in front of the altar, looking up at* WATANABE'S *picture.*

SAKEI : We must work hard.
NOGUCHI : Yes, with the spirit that Mr. Watanabe showed.
SAITO : We mustn't let his death be meaningless.
ONO : Me — I'm going to turn over a new leaf !
NOGUCHI : That's the spirit. Me, I'm going to work for the good of the public !

They are all shouting, waving their arms. Only KIMURA *at the altar is still and silent.*

Fade out.

Fade in to the Citizens' Section as it was at the beginning of the film, only that ONO *is now at* WATANABE'S *desk.* SAKEI *deferentially, glancing back at the information counter, comes to his side.*

SAKEI : Excuse me, but they say that the sewage water has overflowed in Kizaki-cho.
ONO : Well, send them to the Public Works Section.

Cut to KIMURA *looking up sharply at these words.*

Cut to ONO *who stares back.*

Cut to KIMURA. *There is the noise of a chair being pushed over as he stands up.*

ONO *can be seen, glaring at him.*

Cut to KIMURA. *He slowly picks up the chair and sits down. As he sits the camera descends with him. His face is obscured by the documents on his desk. It is as though he is being buried alive in them.*

Cut to SAKEI, *apologetic at the counter.*

SAKEI: Would you please go to the Public Works Section with this?

Cut to the bridge above the park. It is sunset. KIMURA *comes across the bridge on his way home. He stops to look.*

Cut to the park. Children are playing there and their mothers call them in for dinner.

Cut to KIMURA *watching them. He turns and starts off, the camera panning with him. The top of the swing comes into view. The tune,* 'Life Is So Short', *played on a solo flute, is heard over.* KIMURA *walks away.*

Fade out.

END

FILMOGRAPHY

1943 Sanshiro Sugata (Sugata Sanshiro) 80 mins.

Scenario by Akira Kurosawa after the novel by Tsuneo Tomita.
Photographed by Akira Mimura.
Edited by Toshio Goto and Akira Kurosawa.
With Susumu Fujita, Denjiro Okochi, Takashi Shimura, Yukiko Todoroki.

1944 The Most Beautiful (Ichiban Utsukushiku) 85 mins.

Scenario by Akira Kurosawa.
Photographed by Joji Ohara.
With Takashi Shimura, Ichiro Sugai, Yoko Yaguchi, Takako Irie.

1945 Sanshiro Sugata — Part Two (Zoku Sugata Sanshiro) 83 mins.

Scenario by Akira Kurosawa after the novel by Tsuneo Tomita.
Photographed by Hiroshi Suzuki.
With Susumu Fujita, Denjiro Okochi, Ryunosuke Tsukigata, Yukiko Todoroki.

1945 They Who Step on the Tiger's Tail (Tora no O o Fumu Otokotachi 58 mins.

Scenario by Akira Kurosawa after the Kabuki, *Kanjincho*.
Photographed by Takeo Ito.
With Kenichi Enomoto, Denjiro Okochi, Susumu Fujita, Masayuki Mori, Takashi Shimura.
(This film was not released until 1952.)

1946 Those Who Make Tomorrow (Asu o Tsukuru Hitobito) 81 mins.

Scenario by Yusaku Yamagata and Kajiro Yamamoto.
Photographed by Takeo Ito, Mitsui Miura, and Taichi Kankura.
Directed by Kajiro Yamamoto, Hideo Sekigawa, and Akira Kurosawa.
With Kenji Susukida, Chieko Takehisa, Chieko Nakakita.

1946 No Regrets for Our Youth (Waga Seishun ni Kuinashi) 110 mins.

Scenario by Eijiro Hisaita and Akira Kurosawa.
Photographed by Asakazu Nakai.
With Denjiro Okochi, Eiko Miyoshi, Setsuko Hara, Susumu Fujita, Takashi Shimura.

1947 One Wonderful Sunday (Subarashiki Nichiyobi) 108 mins.

Scenario by Keinosuke Uegusa and Akira Kurosawa.
Photographed by Asakazu Nakai.
With Isao Numasaki, Chieko Nakakita, Ichiro Sugai.

1948 Drunken Angel (Yoidore Tenshi) 98 mins.

Scenario by Keinosuke Uegusa and Akira Kurosawa.
Photographed by Takeo Ito.
Music by Fumio Hayasaka.
With Takashi Shimura, Toshiro Mifune, Michiyo Kogure.
(The original 150 min. version was never released.)

1949 The Quiet Duel (Shizukanaru Ketto) 95 mins.

Scenario by Senkichi Taniguchi and Akira Kurosawa, after a play by Kazuo Kikura.
Photographed by Shoichi Aisaka.
With Toshiro Mifune, Takashi Shimura, Chieko Nakakita.

1949 Stray Dog (Nora Inu) 122 mins.
Scenario by Ryuzo Kikushima and Akira Kurosawa.
Photographed by Asakazu Nakai.
Music by Fumio Hayasaka.
With Toshiro Mifune, Takashi Shimura, Ko Kimura.

1950 Scandal (Shubun) 104 mins.
Scenario by Ryuzo Kikushima and Akira Kurosawa.
Photographed by Toshio Ubukata.
Music by Fumio Hayasaka.
With Toshiro Mifune, Yoshiko Yamaguchi, Takashi Shimura.

1950 Rashomon 88 mins.
Scenario by Shinobu Hashimoto and Akira Kurosawa after two stories by Ryunosuke Akutagawa.
Photographed by Kazuo Miyagawa.
Music by Fumio Hayasaka.
With Toshiro Mifune, Masayuki Mori, Machiko Kyo, Takashi Shimura, Minoru Chiaki, Kichijiro Ueda.

1951 The Idiot (Hakuchi) 166 mins.
Scenario by Eijiro Hisaita and Akira Kurosawa after the novel by Dostoevsky.
Photographed by Toshio Ubukata.
Music by Fumio Hayasaka.
With Masayuki Mori, Toshiro Mifune, Setsuko Hara, Takashi Shimura.
(The original 265 min. version was never released.)

1952 Living (Ikiru) 143 mins.
Scenario by Shinobu Hashimoto, Hideo Oguni, and Akira Kurosawa.
Photographed by Asakazu Nakai.
Music by Fumio Hayasaka.
With Takashi Shimura, Miki Odagiri, Yunosuke Ito.

1954 Seven Samurai (Shichinin no Samurai) 160 mins.
Scenario by Shinobu Hashimoto, Hideo Oguni, and Akira Kurosawa.
Photographed by Asakazu Nakai.
Music by Fumio Hayasaka.
With Takashi Shimura, Toshiro Mifune, Yoshio Inaba, Seiji Miyaguchi, Minoru Chiaki, Daisuke Kato, Ko Kimura.
(The original version was 200 mins.)

1955 Record of a Living Being (Ikimono No Kiroku) 104 mins.
Scenario by Shinobu Hashimoto, Hideo Oguni, and Akira Kurosawa.
Photographed by Asakazu Nakai.
With Toshiro Mifune, Takashi Shimura, Minoru Chiaki, Eijiro Tono.
(The original version was 113 mins.)

1957 The Throne of Blood (Kumonosu-jo) 110 mins.
Scenario by Shinobu Hashimoto, Ryuzo Kikushima, Hideo Oguni, and Akira Kurosawa, after Shakespeare's *Macbeth*.
Photographed by Asakazu Nakai.
Music by Masaru Sato.
With Toshiro Mifune, Isuzu Yamada, Minoru Chiaki, Takashi Shimura.

1957 The Lower Depths (Donzoko) 137 mins.
Scenario by Hideo Oguni and Akira Kurosawa after the play by Gorky.
Photographed by Kazuo Yamasaki.
Music by Masaru Sato.
With Toshiro Mifune, Isuzu Yamada, Kyoko Kagawa, Minoru Chiaki, Kamatari Fujiwara, Eijiro Tono.

1958 The Hidden Fortress (Kakushi Toride no San-Akunin) 126 mins.

Scenario by Shinobu Hashimoto, Ryuzo Kikushima, Hideo Oguni, and Akira Kurosawa.
Photographed (widescreen) by Kazuo Yamasaki.
Music by Masaru Sato.
With Toshiro Mifune, Takashi Shimura, Minoru Chiaki, Kamatari Fujiwara, Misa Uehara.
(The original version was 139 mins.)

1960 The Bad Sleep Well (Warui Yatsu Hodo Yoku Nemuru) 135 mins.

Scenario by Shinobu Hashimoto, Hideo Oguni, Ryuzo Kikushima, Eijiro Hisaita, and Akira Kurosawa.
Photographed (widescreen) by Yuzuru Aizawa.
Music by Masaru Sato.
With Toshiro Mifune, Takeshi Kato, Masayuki Mori, Takashi Shimura, Kamatari Fujiwara.
(The original version is 151 mins.)

1961 Yojimbo 110 mins.

Scenario by Ryuzo Kikushima and Akira Kurosawa.
Photographed (widescreen) by Kazuo Miyagawa.
Music by Masaru Sato.
With Toshiro Mifune, Takashi Shimura, Kamatari Fujiwara, Tatsuya Nakadai.

1962 Sanjuro (Tsubaki Sanjuro) 96 mins.

Scenario by Ryuzo Kikushima, Hideo Oguni, and Akira Kurosawa, after the novel by Sungoro Yamamoto.
Photographed (widescreen) by Fukuzo Koizumi.
Music by Mazaru Sato.
With Toshiro Mifune, Tatsuya Nakadai, Takashi Shimura, Kamatari Fujiwara, Takako Irie.

1963 High and Low (Tengoku to Jigoku) 143 mins.
Scenario by Ryuzo Kikushima, Hideo Oguni, and Akira Kurosawa, after an Ed McBain novel.
Photographed (widescreen) by Asakazu Nakai.
Music by Masaru Sato.
With Toshiro Mifune, Kyoko Kagawa, Tatsuya Nakadai, Tsutomu Yamazaki.

1965 Red Beard (Akahige) 185 mins.
Scenario by Ryuzo Kikushima, Hideo Oguni, Masato Ide, and Akira Kurosawa, after the novel by Shugoro Yamamoto.
Photographed (widescreen) by Asakazu Nakai and Takao Saito.
Music by Masaru Sato.
With Toshiro Mifune, Yuzo Kayama, Kyoko Kagawa, Yoshio Tsuchiya.